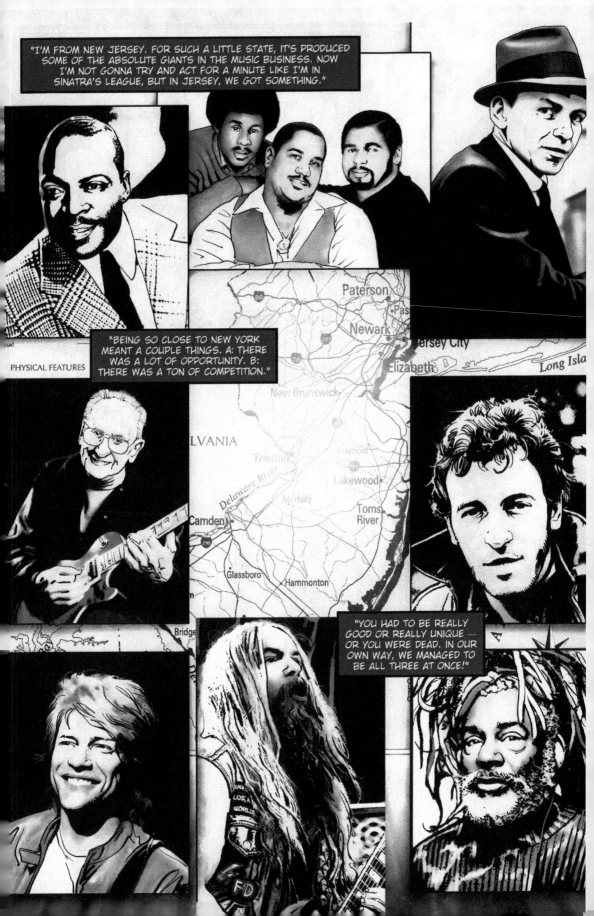

1977. LODI, NEW JERSEY.

NOW IF YOU WANT TO BE TECHNICAL ABOUT IT, I WAS THE SECOND BASS PLAYER IN THE MISFITS. I WAS THE FIRST ONE ON VINYL, THOUGH...

THE RECORD PRESSINGS ARE HERE!

... EVEN IF THEY DID FUCK UP MY NAME.

JERRY " CAIFA?!?" WHAT THE FUCK IS THAT?

GLENN DANZIG - ELECTRIC SYNC-PIANO & VOCALS.
MANNY - DRUMS & PERCUSSION.
JERRY CAIFA - BASS GUITAR

... AND MY ATTEMPT TO FIX IT DIDN'T WORK OUT EXACTLY AS PLANNED.

NO! NO! LISTEN, ASSHOLE! JUST JERRY! JERRY ONLY! WHAT ARE YOU, FUCKIN' DEAF?!?"

GLENN DANZIG - ELECTRIC SYNC-PIANO & VOCALS. MANNY - DRUMS & PERCUSSION. JERRY ONLY - BASS GUITAR

YOU HAVE GOTTA BE KIDDIN' ME.

I DUNNO, I THINK IT SOUNDS COOL.

AND EVER SINCE, THAT'S WHAT IT'S BEEN.

SO WE BROUGHT IN FRANCHÉ COMA ON GUITAR AND STARTED WORK ON THE STATIC AGE ALBUM.

ONETWOTHREEFOUR-

WE WERE REALLY RIPPIN' SHIT UP TOO — BUT I WASN'T SURE ABOUT SOME OF THE LYRIC CHOICES.

SERIOUSLY? "MASTURBATE ME?"

HOW ABOUT YOU PLAY THE BASS AND LET ME HANDLE THE FUCKIN' WORDS. SEE ALL THE PEOPLE AT THE GIGS LATELY? SHIT'S GOING GOOD — DON'T FUCK WITH IT!

SON OF A BITCH WAS RIGHT THOUGH — PEOPLE WERE DIGGING IT.

WE ADDED BOBBY STEELE AND JOEY IMAGE TO THE LINEUP, RELEASED THE HORROR BUSINESS EP, AND LEANED INTO THE HORROR ANGLE HARD.

HORROR BUSINESS ONETWO~

TAKE ONE TEENAGERS FROM MARS AND CHILDREN IN HEAT ONETWOTHREEFOUR~

AND THEN, UP AT THIS THRIFT STORE IN THE CITY, WE FOUND OUR MASCOT. TOTAL FUCKIN' DESTINY.

THIS SKULL IS FUCKIN' BADASS.

WHERE'S DANZIG? TOO GOOD TO DO THE FUCKIN' GRUNT WORK?

ACTUALLY ASSHOLE I WAS GETTING US A FUCKIN' GIG! MAX'S KANSAS CITY OPENING UP FOR THE MOTHERFUCKIN' DAMNED!

GET THE FUCK OUTTA HERE. THE DAMNED! HOLY SHIT!

THAT'S FUCKIN' BIG, MAN.

IT WAS A MISCOMMUNICATION, WHAT CAN YOU DO? ALL THE TOUR MANAGER WOULD GIVE US WAS THESE BULLSHIT 15 MINUTE SETS AT THE VERY BEGINNING OF THE SHOW. TOOK LONGER TO SET UP THE AMPS THAN TO PLAY THE FUCKIN' SET! DANZIG COULDN'T DEAL, AND WE BAILED AFTER 2 NIGHTS.

WE STOPPED BY SID VICIOUS' HOUSE, BUT HE WASN'T AROUND. HIS MOM WAS THERE THOUGH, LET US CRASH THERE FOR THE NIGHT. SHE ASKED US IF WE KNEW WHERE SID WAS, BUT WE HAD NO IDEA. TURNS OUT HE WAS OUT PARTYING AND DIED LIKE 2 DAYS LATER.

GLENN WAS PISSED OFF ABOUT THE TOUR AND PICKED A FIGHT WITH A SKINHEAD CREW THE NEXT DAY.

THE FUCK ARE YOU FUCKIN' ASSHOLES LOOKING AT? YOU WANNA FUCKIN' GO?

THIS IS FUCKIN' BULLSHIT. TRYING TO GET OUR FUCKIN' NAME OUT THERE AND INSTEAD WE WIND UP IN A LONDON FUCKIN' DUNGEON.

"LONDON DUNGEON." HUH.

FINALLY MADE IT BACK TO JERSEY AND GOT RIGHT TO WORK ON THE "BEWARE" EP. MY LITTLE BROTHER PAUL WANTED TO SEE US REHEARSE. WHAT WAS I GONNA SAY, NO?

HALLOWEEN! ONETWOTHREEFOUR-

LOOK AT HIM PRACTICING' AWAY IN THERE. MEANWHILE FUCKIN' BOBBY HERE LOOKS LIKE HE'D RATHER BE GETTIN' A FUCKIN' ROOT CANAL.

I DECIDED MY BROTHER SHOULD JOIN THE BAND, BUT THE ONLY WAY TO DO THAT WAS TO GET BOBBY TO LEAVE.

HEY BOBBY - PRACTICE IS CANCELLED TONIGHT. YEAH, AGAIN. I DON'T KNOW, GLENN HAD TO BE SOMEWHERE. OK YOU GOT IT. I'LL LET YOU KNOW.

WHERE THE FUCK IS BOBBY? THIS IS THE FOURTH FUCKIN' PRACTICE HE SKIPPED!

MUST THINK HE'S TOO GOOD TO REHEARSE. HEY PAUL, YOU KNOW ALL THE SONGS, RIGHT?

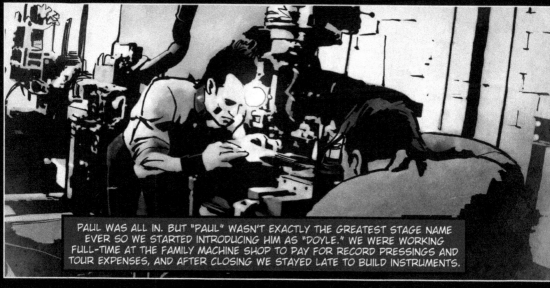

PAUL WAS ALL IN. BUT "PAUL" WASN'T EXACTLY THE GREATEST STAGE NAME EVER SO WE STARTED INTRODUCING HIM AS "DOYLE." WE WERE WORKING FULL-TIME AT THE FAMILY MACHINE SHOP TO PAY FOR RECORD PRESSINGS AND TOUR EXPENSES, AND AFTER CLOSING WE STAYED LATE TO BUILD INSTRUMENTS.

AND THE INSTRUMENTS WE BUILT WERE FUCKIN' BADASS.

GLENN MOSTLY STAYED HOME WRITING LYRICS AND RUNNING THE FIEND CLUB.

"STAY COOL, GHOUL! - DANZIG"

FUCK, MAN. THIS SHIT IS LIKE BORDERLINE SATANIC.

ARE YOU KIDDING ME RIGHT NOW?

FOR THE LAST FUCKING TIME, I WRITE THE LYRICS, ASSHOLE! YOU GOT A PROBLEM, FUCKIN' WALK!

HOLY SHIT! THE FUCK IS WRONG WITH YOU GUYS?

MAYBE WE DIDN'T GET ALONG THAT GREAT, BUT YOU BETTER BELIEVE WE TOOK THE BAND SERIOUS. BUT ONE NIGHT ALL OUR PROFESSIONALISM WENT RIGHT OUT THE WINDOW, THANKS TO A PISS DRUNK DRUMMER.

NIKE! ONETWO~

CRASH!!!

THIS IS A TOTAL FUCKIN' SHITSHOW.

HEY ASSHOLES, LISTEN UP! I GOT SOMETHING TO SAY. THIS... IS OUR LAST SHOW. THE MISFITS ARE FUCKIN' DONE.

WE DROVE HOME THAT NIGHT, DIDN'T SAY A WORD TO EACH OTHER IN THE CAR, AND AS FAR AS WE WERE CONCERNED, THAT WAS IT. WE'D BEEN SICK OF EACH OTHER FOR YEARS, THIS WAS JUST THE FINAL STRAW.

WE CAN'T EVEN BOOK A SHOW AS "THE MISFITS" WITHOUT LAWYERS SHUTTING US DOWN 'CAUSE DANZIG OWNS THE NAME. ISN'T DOING SHIT WITH IT, MIND YOU — JUST SITTING ON THE NAME WATCHING THE MONEY COME IN. WE FOUGHT IN COURT FOR YEARS...

I WROTE THE LYRICS, I WROTE THE MUSIC, AND I OWN THE RECORD LABEL. THE REST OF THE BAND WERE HIRED GUNS AND THEY WERE PAID FOR THEIR TIME. I DON'T OWE THEM ANYTHING AND THEY''RE NOT ENTITLED TO ANYTHING.

GLENN WROTE ALL THE WORDS, YOUR HONOR, SURE. BUT HE ABSOLUTELY DID NOT WRITE ALL THE MUSIC. THAT WAS A GROUP EFFORT. WE ALL CONTRIBUTED. WE ALL DESERVE A STAKE IN THE OWNERSHIP.

DANZIG WAS NOT GOING TO BUDGE ON SONGWRITING CREDIT, AND I WAS TIRED OF THE BULLSHIT SO EVENTUALLY I JUST DECIDED TO LET HIM HAVE IT. WE SETTLED OUT-OF-COURT.

BOTTOM LINE IS WE FINALLY HAVE THE RIGHT TO RECORD AND PERFORM AS THE MISFITS, AND HAVE A SHARE IN THE MERCHANDISE SALES. THE MISFITS HAVE RISEN FROM THE GRAVE!

SO IT WAS ME, DOYLE, NEW SINGER MICHAELE GRAVES AND DR. CHUD ON DRUMS. THE NEW ALBUM AMERICAN PSYCHO WAS THE BEST THING I HAD EVER PUT ON RECORD UP TO THAT POINT.

WE DID A WORLD TOUR WITH MEGADETH JUST IN TIME FOR OUR TWENTIETH ANNIVERSARY.

WE EVEN MADE TV APPEARANCES WITH VAMPIRO ON WCW WRESTLING! ALL OF A SUDDEN, WE WERE FUCKIN' EVERYWHERE!

BUT NOTHING GOOD EVER SEEMS TO LAST TOO LONG. GRAVES AFTER A WHILE JUST DIDN'T WANT TO BE THERE ANYMORE, SO I CUT HIM LOOSE.

THEN DOYLE TOOK A BREAK FROM THE BAND. THAT WAS A ROLLER COASTER. ARM PROBLEMS, THEN A DIVORCE, THEN REMARRIED, AND THEN CAME BABY #4. I WOULDA NEED A BREAK TOO!

BUT I DIDN'T WANNA JUST FUCKIN' SIT HOME AND ROT. I CALLED DANZIG TO SEE IF HE WANTED TO DO SOME REUNION DATES, BUT HE WASN'T INTO IT.

HELLO, GLENN? HELLO?

I EVEN TRIED DAVE VANIAN FROM THE DAMNED, TO SEE IF HE MIGHT BE INTO IT...

I'LL NEED TO START "LIFTING" YOU SAY? SO I CAN "BULK UP?" OH MY — WELL ACTUALLY, WE'RE REFORMING THE DAMNED, SO WHILE I'M EXTRAORDINARILY FLATTERED, I'M AFRAID I'LL HAVE TO DECLINE.

WHEN I START "LIFTING" SO I "BULK UP" HE SAYS...

PFFT.

BUT WHAT REALLY BROADSIDED ME WAS WHEN I FOUND OUT DOYLE STARTED A WHOLE NEW BAND AND WAS ON TOUR OPENING FOR FUCKING DANZIG. PLAYING MISFITS SONGS WITH HIM.

iMac

THINGS WERE GOING GREAT, AND THEN GLENN AND I STARTED TALKING AGAIN. I DON'T KNOW WHY IT WORKED, BUT IT DID.

MAYBE WHEN HE SAW THAT I COULD DO IT WITHOUT HIM HE FINALLY RESPECTED ME A LITTLE BIT. BETTER LATE THAN NEVER. EITHER WAY, THE ORIGINAL MISFITS ARE PLAYING SHOWS AGAIN.

WE JUST DO ONE-NIGHTERS HERE AND THERE SO IT'LL NEVER NOT BE AN EVENT. MEANWHILE GLENN TOURS WITH DANZIG, DOYLE TOURS WITH HIS BAND, I RUN THE MISFITS, AND WHOEVER IT IS, THE FANS COME SEE US WHENEVER WE'RE IN TOWN.

WHOOA-OH-OH!

WHOOA-OH-OH!

WHOOA-OH-OH!

TIDALWAVE
COMICS

Joe Paradise — Writer

Martin Gimenez — Art

Benjamin Glibert — Letters

Darren G. Davis — Editor

Martin Gimenez & Joe Paradise — Covers

Darren G. Davis
Publisher

Maggie Jessup
Publicity

Susan Ferris
Entertainment Manager

Steven Diggs Jr.
Marketing Manager

TIDALWAVE
PRODUCTIONS

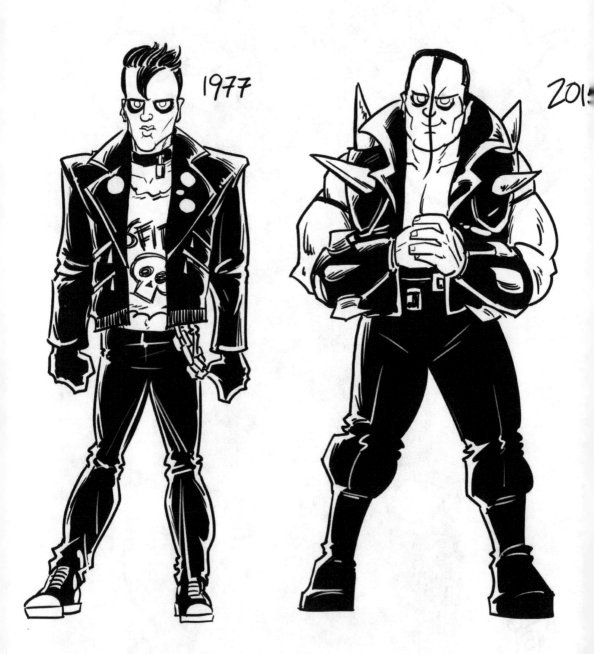

1977

201

1977
2015